SOMETIMES I WORRY TOO MUCH, BUT NOW I KNOW HOW TO STOP

A Book To Help Children Who Worry When They Don't Need To

By Dawn A. Huebner, Ph.D.

Childswork™
ChildsPLAY

CALL 1•800•962•1141

A Brand of The Guidance Group
www.guidance-group.com

**Sometimes I Worry Too Much,
But Now I Know How To Stop**

By Dawn A. Huebner, Ph.D.
Illustrated by Robin C. Morris

Childswork/Childsplay publishes products for mental health professionals, teachers, and parents who wish to help children with their developmental, social, and emotional growth. For questions, comments, or to request a free catalog describing hundreds of games, toys, books, and other counseling tools, call 1-800-962-1141.

No part of this book may be reproduced or transmitted in any form or by any means, electronic or mechanical, including photocopying, recording, or by any information storage and retrieval system without written permission from the publisher.

© 2003 Childswork/Childsplay
A Brand of The Guidance Group
1.800.962.1141
www.guidance-group.com

Printed in the United States of America

ISBN 10: 1-58815-060-7
ISBN 13: 978-1-58815-060-8

Introduction

Excessive worrying is a serious problem for a significant number of children and many adults as well. It is a myth that childhood should be "worry-free." It is normal for children to worry about things like being invited to a party, doing well on a test, or trying out for a sports team. It is also normal for children to worry about bigger issues, like the state of their parents' marriage or the serious illness of a close relative or friend.

But worrying becomes excessive when children are concerned about things that are really not problems. Excessive worry should also be considered a symptom of a deeper problem when children are overwhelmed by their worry, even if there is a legitimate reason for it. Worrying should always be seen as a serious problem when it consumes a significant part of a child's thoughts and influences his or her day-to-day behavior.

Like Anna, the girl in this story, many children who worry excessively are very sensitive. They notice things that other children might ignore, and they interpret what they see in the most negative way possible. It is as if they are looking at the world through a magnifying glass, but that magnifying glass has a distorted lens. Rather than seeing the world objectively, they focus on potential problems. More importantly, when these children see a problem, real or imagined, they do not see its solution. Thinking about the problem over and over again can feel like a solution to children who worry, but it obviously is not. Excessive worry keeps such children in a constant state of stress and hypervigilance, which can lead to psychosomatic problems or actual physical health problems. Too often, excessive worrying in children can lead to a lifetime of emotional distress.

As with all mental and physical health problems, an ounce of prevention is worth a pound of cure. Early treatment of children who worry too much is essential. This engaging book by Dr. Dawn A. Huebner can be used to help children see that there is help for excessive worrying. Like Anna, most children benefit from simple cognitive and behavioral techniques. Sometimes medication is useful when symptoms are severe and the worrying affects the child's school performance, social life, or other important aspects of development. A comprehensive evaluation and treatment plan is always the first step for children with emotional problems.

It is important to get early and effective help for children who worry too much. We hope that this book will be a step in that direction.

Lawrence E. Shapiro, Ph.D.
Series Editor

This book is part of the "Sometimes" series of books for helping children develop a positive attitude towards solving their mental health problems. The series also includes:

- Sometimes I Feel Like I Don't Have Any Friends, But Not So Much Anymore

- Sometimes I Like to Fight, But I Don't Do It Much Anymore

- Sometimes I Drive My Mom Crazy, But I Know She's Crazy About Me

- Sometimes I Get Sad, But Now I Know What Makes Me Happy

- Sometimes I Don't Like to Talk, But Sometimes I Can't Keep Quiet

What if I go down for breakfast and we are all out of cream cheese? I can't eat my bagel without cream cheese.

What if Hope still has a sore throat tomorrow? Who will I play with at recess?

My name is Anna. I used to worry a lot.

My mom always told me that everything was going to be okay. My dad said, "Don't worry, be happy!" I think that's a line from a song he used to like. Everyone told me that I worried way too much, but I couldn't help it. Worries would just pop into my head, and then what was I supposed to do?

I've always been a kid who notices things.

When my mom has the tiniest little frown, I see it and then I wonder if she's mad at me. I notice when the sky is getting gray, and I can spot a spider from all the way across the room.

One day, my Grandpa Dan was reading the newspaper while Grandma and I played Go Fish. I saw the word "FIRE" right on the front page of Grandpa Dan's newspaper. It was one of my spelling words, so I recognized it right away.

I got to thinking about fires and worrying that my house might burn down. All of a sudden, I couldn't remember if I had already asked Grandma if she had any fives. The game just wasn't fun anymore.

Around the same time, my stomach started to hurt—not just once in a while, but every day. I told my mom and my teacher and the nurse at my school. Mom took me to Dr. Matthews, but he said that I was "healthy as a horse" and that my stomachache was all in my head. That made me kind of mad because it wasn't my head that hurt, it was my stomach!

It seemed like no one believed me.

Things got worse after that.

I didn't want to go to Hope's house anymore, and she's my best friend. I started following Mom and Dad around, because I hated to be alone in a room. If I was by myself, I got a nervous feeling inside.

Dad started to call me the "What If Kid" because I asked tons of questions, and they always seemed to start with "what if." What if I forget to put my homework in my backpack? What if our dog Topper gets sick? What if we run out of money for food?

My parents always answered my questions, but I still felt worried a lot of the time.

My mom took me back to Dr. Matthews. It was time for my checkup, anyway.

When Mom told Dr. Matthews what was going on, he said my body was still as healthy as could be, but my head was chock-full of worries. Dr. Matthews told us about his friend, Dr. Green. She's a different kind of doctor, called a psychologist. Her job is to help kids like me who worry too much.

Dr. Green was really nice. She asked me about school and my friends. She wanted to know what made me happy. She listened to all the things I worried about. She even believed me about my stomachaches. I liked it best when we drew pictures.

Dr. Green told me that worries are like stones. Most people hardly notice them, but I do. I see them, and then I pick them up and put them in my pocket.

I looked at her kind of funny because I didn't know what she meant.

She said to imagine that each worry was a little stone. I was carrying around hundreds of stones, and it wasn't much fun because they were way too heavy. Dr. Green said that as long as there were so many stones in my pockets, there wasn't room for anything else.

She said she was going to help me learn to empty my pockets. I think she meant she was going to help me not carry around so many worries.

I thought that was a really good idea.

Dr. Green asked me what was the most comfortable chair in my house. She asks strange questions sometimes.

Our most comfortable chair is in my dad's office. It is brown and really soft, and there is a special handle you can move to make the foot part go up. Dr. Green said that the brown chair should be my worry chair. Each night after dinner, Mom or Dad should go into the office with me for some worry time. I would get to sit in the brown chair and talk about whatever worries were bothering me. Mom and Dad would talk to me about my worries and try to help me feel better.

There were just two rules that we needed to follow. The first rule is that I would only get to sit in the brown chair and talk about my worries for 15 minutes. After that, worry time was over. The other rule is that I could only talk about worries when I was in the brown chair.

The second rule was the hardest, because I was so used to talking about my worries whenever they popped into my head. Dr. Green reminded me to think of each worry as a stone. If I felt worried about something during the day, I should imagine bringing the stone to Dad's office to put by the brown chair until our worry time that night.

Mom and Dad helped me. They reminded me to turn my daytime worries into stones (in my mind, of course). We had our worry time every night.

Sometimes, I had a lot of worries to talk about, and sometimes I didn't. After we had been doing it for a while, I noticed something. Most nights, by the time we got to worry time, I had forgotten about some of my worries.

Dr. Green said that was okay. Worries often go away when you don't think about them, and that's a good thing—like emptying out your pockets.

After I had practiced turning worries into stones and putting them aside until worry time, Dr. Green taught me about jumping hurdles. She said that when someone worries, it is like they are walking along when, all of a sudden, a big roadblock gets in the way. Kids who worry too much crash into the roadblock and fall down. They need to learn how to jump over the roadblock and continue on their way.

Dr. Green and I practiced jumping over roadblocks. We listed my worries, and then we talked about how to solve them. Dr. Green told me I was good at solving worries. Whenever she asked, "Well, what would you do if you were out of cream cheese or if Hope was out sick?" I could always think of an answer.

One day, when I wasn't even with Dr. Green, I started to wonder, "What if my dad forgets to pick me up after school?" But instead of getting stuck behind the worry like I used to, I just thought about how I could go into the office and ask the secretary to call him. That wouldn't be so bad.

When I didn't want to go upstairs alone to brush my teeth, I told myself that my house was a safe place, and besides, I could call out for Mom if I really needed her.

Whenever I had a worry, instead of just getting stuck behind the "what if" hurdle, I jumped right over it. I thought about how I could handle whatever I was worrying about, if it really did happen. I started to tell myself that it would be okay.

Mom and Dad and Dr. Green were proud of me because I didn't ask as many "what if" questions anymore. I was proud of myself, too. Jumping hurdles in my mind felt good.

I was worrying a lot less than I used to and answering most of my own "what if" questions, but some worries were still getting stuck in my brain.

Dr. Green told me that it was time to learn about the brain eraser. She said that even though worries just pop into my mind, I get to decide whether or not to let them stay there.

Dr. Green taught me to imagine that I had a magical brain eraser. Whatever I didn't want in my mind, I could wipe away with my brain eraser, like cleaning off the chalkboard in my classroom.

I like that trick because I get to use my imagination. When a really stubborn worry is bothering me, I picture it like a drawing in my mind. Then I grab my brain eraser (mine is black and looks like a chalkboard eraser, but yours can look however you want it to) and wipe it out.

Dr. Green told me that after I erase the worry, I should get busy thinking about or doing something else. I can draw a castle in my mind or plan my next birthday party. I can join in a game of tag, or read a book, or play with Topper. If I'm at school, I can listen to what the teacher is saying or think about my work.

It is nice to have a choice about whether or not to keep thinking about my worries. Mostly I decide to use the brain eraser, because worries aren't much fun to think about.

I've been noticing a few things lately. I really like going to Hope's house again, and I've even made some new friends. I've been falling asleep faster at night, and when I wake up, I think about the things I am looking forward to that day. My stomach hardly ever hurts—except when I've talked Mom into giving me an extra dessert!

It seems like I am having more fun, since I've learned to stop worrying so much. Dr. Green says that worrying takes a lot of time and energy. I know what she means. Dr. Green also said that I don't need to come see her so often anymore. She said that if I felt like I needed to talk, I should tell Mom or Dad and they could call her.

I still feel worried once in a while. When I can't solve my worries on my own, I ask for some worry time in the brown chair. But my worries go away a lot faster than they used to, instead of getting stuck in my mind. I like that.

I bet that you can learn to make most of your worries go away, too.

The End